by
Ruth Kenward and Jo Sands

(arr. Mark Dickman)

www.starshine.co.uk

Brown Cottage, Hankham, East Sussex, England. BN24 5BJ.
Tel: +44 (0)1323 764334   Fax: +44 (0)1323 767145   E-mail: info@starshine.co.uk

Grateful acknowledgement is due to the following schools/groups who took part in pre-publication trials:
Ashbury CEP School, Wiltshire   Askern Spa Junior School, South Yorkshire
Holy Cross RCP School, Bristol   Church-in-the-Wood Primary School, E.Sussex
Grovelands Community School, E. Sussex   Sacred Heart Catholic Primary School, W. Yorkshire

ISBN: 1-90-559114-4   978-1-90-559114-5

Director's Notes

The cast requires 6 main characters, and 20 other scripted speaking parts, some of which can be shared between 2-3 children if required. The chorus may be extended as required to meet the needs of larger groups.

MAIN CHARACTERS

Kim	Gang leader, tough, mean
Frankie	Kim's sidekick, also a very strong character
Ruby	A gang member, Ellie's 'sponsor'
Ellie	Wants to be in the gang
Danny	Kim's younger brother
Jake	Same age as Danny, victim of the gang's bullying

OTHER CHARACTERS

Girl 1,2,3,4	Four gang members are scripted, but lines can be shared if needed, making a larger 'gang' group
Child 1,2,3,4	Jake's friends
Ant	Jake's friend
Teacher	Sympathetic to Jake, only appears in one scene
Ellie's Mum & Dad	Ellie's parents, who only appear in one scene
Rachel	Ellie's older sister, who is very unpleasant, bullying Ellie
Mother, Father Son, Daughter	Stereotypical happy family, who appear in one scene
Matt, Josh	Police officers
Laura, Amy	" "

PROPS

Scene 1: sweets for gang, mobile phone for Jake
Scene 3: Table & chair for Ellie's house. Schoolbook for Ellie.
Scene 4: backpacks for Jake & Danny containing coats and water bottles. Coins for Jake's pockets
Scene 6: bottles of drink for Jake and Danny, large boxes for warehouse containing plenty of costumes, including pop star outfit & wig for Laura, tutu for Josh, Charlie Chaplin hat and stick for Amy.

STAGING SUGGESTIONS

A street environment needs to be suggested for most of the scenes, but, unless you have the facility to make major scene changes, this should be done in a reasonably minimal way.

The street might be suggested by positioning a signpost to one side, indicating town centre directions such as 'Bus Station', 'Town Hall', 'Toilets', etc. You might also include a couple of shop window flats, an advertisement billboard, a bus-stop, etc. Graffiti on a brick wall backdrop is effective. There are also scene switches to Ellie's house and warehouse interiors, which may be achieved as follows: Ellie's house can be suggested by simply bringing a couple of chairs and a table to centre stage, and placing other household props with them. The warehouse can be suggested by placing several packing cases or large cardboard boxes upstage right. These need to be positioned so that Jake and Danny can hide in one place, while the police officers can rummage in other boxes nearby.

2

Director's Overview

<u>SCENE 1</u>   (p. 5) On the street. Ellie becomes a bully.

SONG - WHERES KIM?   (◉ Track 1 / 16)

Ellie earns a place in Kim's gang by bullying Jake into giving her his mobile phone.

SONG - IN THE GANG   (◉ Track 2 / 17)

<u>SCENE 2</u>   (p. 8) The street. People try to cheer Jake up, first a teacher, then some police officers (who we learn are going to a fancy dress party later on). Then Jake tells some friends what has happened. They all wish they were as strong and brave as superheroes.

SONG - REAL TOUGH STUFF   (◉ Track 3 / 18)

<u>SCENE 3</u>   (p. 12) Ellie's house Ellie's parents are going out. Ellie is being 'babysat' by her older sister, Rachel. We discover that Rachel is bullying Ellie.

SAD STUFF - incidental   (◉ Track 4 / 19)

TOUGH STUFF - incidental   (◉ Track 5 / 20)

<u>SCENE 4</u>   (p. 13) The street. Jake's money is stolen by Ellie and her friend Ruby, who have another go at him. Jake is miserable, and wishes he could change things.

SONG - MAKE TIME GO BACKWARDS   (◉ Track 6 / 21)

Jake tells his friend Danny he wants to run away. Danny says he'll show him a great place to hide.

<u>SCENE 5</u>   (p. 17) In the street on Saturday, with the gang and others. Jake's friends confront Kim's gang, asking for Jake's phone to be returned.

SONG - SATURDAY   (◉ Track 7 / 22)

Kim is devastated that her brother Danny has gone missing. The gang offer to help her look for him.

SONG - OUT THERE   (◉ Track 8 / 23)

<u>SCENE 6</u>   (p.20) In the warehouse. Danny and Jake pass a happy family in the street before going into the warehouse.   The boys realise that they will be in trouble already by this time, so decide to stay overnight in the warehouse.

BACKWARDS - incidental   (◉ Track 9 / 24)

<u>SCENE 7</u>   (p. 22) The dressing-up scene The police officers arrive at the warehouse and try on costumes that are stored there.

SONG - SOMEONE ELSE'S EYES   (◉ Track 10 / 25)

The boys are nearly discovered after Danny coughs, but then the officers leave.

SONG - OUT THERE (short reprise)   (◉ Track 11 / 26)

<u>SCENE 8</u>   (p. 26) The warehouse, early next day. The boys wake up. Danny goes outside to buy food, and meets his sister Kim and her gang in the street. She's delighted to find him. He explains that his friend has been bullied, and that's why they ran away. In the warehouse, Danny is horrified to discover his own sister is the leader of the gang that bullied his friend.

MORNING MUSIC - incidental   (◉ Track 12 / 27)

Danny is ashamed of Kim, but Jake persuades him to give her another chance, as the gang have explained that they all became bullies because they had been bullied themselves. Ellie gives Jake back his phone, and they decide to confront her sister, Rachel, to see what turned her into a bully.

SONG - BULLY!   (◉ Track 13 / 28)

<u>SCENE 9</u>   (p. 30) In the street, Jake and Ellie confront Rachel backed up by the gang.

SONG - WRONG AIN'T RIGHT   (◉ Track 14 / 29)

Rachel and Ellie are reconciled.

SONG - REAL TOUGH STUFF (reprise)   (◉ Track 15 / 30)

SCENE 1   School Playground, Ellie becomes a bully.

Kim's gang gather together with a general atmosphere of laughter, slightly aggressive play, noise.

WHERE'S KIM?   (⊙ Track 1 / 16)

Chorus	WHERE'S KIM? *(four times)*
Girl 1	Where's Kim?
Girl 2	Yeah, where is she?
Gang	Late, as usual...
Girl 1	Has anyone seen her yet?
Girl 3	Not me...
Girl 1	Ruby, have you seen her?
Ruby	Nah, but she'll be here soon.
Girl 1	What about you Frankie? Have you seen 'er?
Frankie	Not since yesterday...
Girl 3	Lazy thing, still in bed!
Gang	Ooh! Better not let Kim hear you say that!
Frankie	SHE'S OUR NUMBER ONE.
Chorus	THAT'S KIM.
Frankie	SHE ALWAYS GETS THINGS DONE.
Chorus	THAT'S KIM.
Frankie	AN' NOTHING MAKES HER FEAR.
Chorus	THAT'S KIM.
Gang	THAT IS WHY WE NEED HER HERE.
Gang	WE KNOW WE'RE OK
Chorus	WITH KIM.
Gang	'COS TROUBLE'S KEPT AT BAY
Chorus	WITH KIM.
Gang	AN' NOTHING MAKES US FEAR
Chorus	WITH KIM.
ALL	THAT IS WHY WE NEED HER HERE.
	'COS SHE LEADS US, SHE LEADS US:
	THAT'S OUR KIM.
	(pointing) THAT'S OUR KIM!

Enter Kim ←

Kim	*(with a grand gesture)* HERE I AM!

[Ad lib responses from GANG, e.g. 'Hi, Kim! Where've you been?' etc. RUBY whispers to GIRL 2 then exits]

Kim	*(with authority)* Ok, who's got the sweets?
Frankie	'Ere, have one of these. I nicked 'em off a first year.
Kim	*(laughs)* Nice one!

Girl 2	YOU'RE THE BOSS.
Kim	THAT'S A FACT I DON'T DENY.
Girl 2	DON'T BE CROSS.
Kim	OH COME ON - JUST TELL ME WHY!
Girl 2	THERE'S THIS GIRL.
Kim	WHAT ABOUT HER? WHAT'S HER NAME?
Girl 2	WE LET HER INTO THE GANG.

Kim	*(spoken)* In our gang?
Gang	THAT'S A FACT WE DON'T DENY.
Kim	*(spoken)* Now I am cross.
Gang	WON'T YOU LET US TELL YOU WHY...
Kim	*(spoken)* Go on then...
Gang	SHE'S RUBY'S FRIEND AND SHE'S OK.
Kim	*(spoken)* I say who gets in the gang.
Chorus	SHE SAYS WHO GETS IN THE GANG.
Kim	*(spoken)* Who is she anyway?

[Enter RUBY with ELLIE, both looking nervous]

Chorus	*(pointing)* ELLIE JONES.
Gang	SHE'S THE ONE FROM FRANKLYN STREET.
Chorus	ELLIE JONES.
Gang	MESSY HAIR AND SMELLY FEET! *(Ellie reacts)*
Chorus	ELLIE JONES.
Gang	RUBY TOLD US ELLIE'S FINE -
ALL	WE THOUGHT THAT YOU WOULDN'T MIND.
	(pointing at RUBY) SHE THOUGHT THAT YOU WOULDN'T MIND!

Kim	*(to RUBY)* YOU KNOW WHAT I SAID,
	IT'S ME MAKES THE RULES.
	SHE'D BETTER BE GOOD
	(to GANG generally) OR YOU'LL LOOK LIKE FOOLS.
Kim/Frankie	SHE MUST PASS THE TEST,
	BE AS GOOD AS THE REST.
	SHE MUST PROVE SHE'S WORTHY,
	WORTHY TO BE WITH THE BEST.
Gang/Chorus	YEAH, SHE MUST PROVE SHE'S WORTHY,
	WORTHY TO BE WITH US, WITH US, WITH US.

(sung to ELLIE)
IF YOU WANT TO BECOME ONE OF US
THEN YOU MUST DO WHAT SHE SAYS
EVERY TIME. NEVER WHINE!
DON'T YOU EVER MAKE A FUSS
TO BECOME ONE OF US,

*(getting steadily faster and louder
as they crowd around ELLIE)*
ONE OF US, ONE OF US, ONE OF US, ONE OF US,
ONE OF US, ONE OF US, ONE OF US.

> *Dramatic effect is more important than accuracy of timing.*

[As the song ends JAKE & ANT enter, JAKE holding a mobile phone. They make it obvious they are wary of Kim's gang, staying as far away as possible from the gang, looking slightly nervous.]

KIM	Watch and learn, Ellie.

[ELLIE nods nervously, putting her hands in her pockets.]

GIRL 1	Hey, you know that girl who just got a new pair of _____ *(popular brand name)* trainers?
KIM	What girl? I don't remember.
GIRL 1	Oh Kim, you <u>know</u>! She was going <u>on</u> and <u>on</u> about them yesterday!
KIM	Oh <u>her</u>!
GIRL 1	Well, guess who took them for a swim in the toilet?!

[General laughter]

KIM	Good one!
GIRL 1	*(grinning and gesturing towards the boys)* Anyone want a free phone?
RUBY	*(to ELLIE)* Now's your chance.
KIM	Yeah. Get that phone and you're in. But you're on your own.
GIRL 2/3	Go, Ellie! Go, Ellie!

[GANG scatter to the sides of the stage 'hiding' to watch what happens. ELLIE advances towards the boys.]

ANT	Uh-oh, this looks like trouble!
JAKE	Come on, let's go!

[They start to go but ELLIE gets in front of them fast and stands preventing their departure, hands on hips. ANT manages to dodge out of the way and runs off.]

ELLIE	*(indicating mobile phone)* Give!
JAKE	No, it's mine!
ELLIE	Not any more. I said <u>give</u>! *(grabbing the arm of Jake's tee shirt)* Of course I could always rip this off... Then what would Mummy's boy do?

JAKE	Hey! Please give it back... Come on... *(continue protesting ad lib until Ellie starts talking on the phone)*

[*ELLIE grabs the phone and dials a number.*]

ELLIE	*(into phone)* Hi! It's me. .....Yeah..... Got a new mobile... Yeah.....OK.
JAKE	<u>Please</u> don't use all my credit... I'm supposed to save it for emergencies!
ELLIE	*(to JAKE sarcastically)* This <u>is</u> an emergency. *(to caller)* See ya. *(Rings off.)*
JAKE	We haven't got much money....
ELLIE	Well you don't have a phone bill now, 'cos you haven't got a phone!
JAKE	Oh, please...
ELLIE	Get lost, you're making the place look untidy.

[*JAKE looks at her for a moment, then shrugs and goes.*
The rest of the GANG come forward. KIM grins at ELLIE]

KIM	Nice one!
RUBY	Yeah, you did well!

[*General agreement, nods, etc.*]

ELLIE	Thanks!
KIM	You're in.

<u>IN THE GANG</u>   (☉ Track 2 / 17)

Gang NOW YOU ARE ONE OF US,
REALLY ARE ONE OF US.
AND NONE OF US
WILL LET YOU DOWN,
YOU CAN BE SURE
YOU'RE SAFE WITH US
'COS YOU'RE IN!

The song should burst into life here.

ALL SHE'S IN THE GANG,
SHE'S REALLY IN THE GANG NOW.
SHE PASSED THE TEST,
'COS THE GIRLS WERE WELL IMPRESSED.
NOW SHE'S IN,
IT'S SINK OR SWIM.
IN THE GANG,
SHE'S REALLY IN THE GANG NOW.
THAT'S ALL IT TOOK
TO GET IN TO THEIR GOOD BOOKS.

GANG exit, miming chatter and laughter, looking at mobile, eating sweets etc.

7

NOW SHE'S IN,
IT'S SINK OR SWIM.
THROUGH THICK AND THIN
SHE MUST KEEP IN.
'COS SHE IS ONE OF THEM,
ONE OF THEM, ONE OF THEM.

SCENE 2   People try to cheer Jake up

JAKE enters looking depressed. He sits on the floor to one side, huddled up with hands clasped around his legs, chin on his knees. TEACHER enters and sees him.

TEACHER	It's Jake isn't it? From Class 6?
JAKE	Yes, Sir. *(or Miss)*
TEACHER	Why are you sitting there all by yourself?
JAKE	*(unconvincingly, as he gets up)* Oh... no reason...
TEACHER	*(not believing him)* Really?

> *[JAKE nods his head. During following dialogue two pairs of uniformed police constables enter, MATT & LAURA from Upstage R. JOSH & AMY from Upstage L. They meet centre stage, miming conversation until TEACHER exits.]*

TEACHER	Sometimes it helps to share your problems.

> *[Silence. JAKE looks at the floor.]*

Well, if you need a chat you can always come and see me at school. What d'you think?

> *[JAKE shrugs]*

Well, it's up to you. I'm there if you need me.

> *[TEACHER walks away, looking concerned. JAKE moves in opposite direction, then sits down when Teacher's gone.]*

AMY	Are you three still coming to the party tonight?
LAURA	Dunno. I'd like to, but I haven't sorted out a costume yet.
JOSH	These fancy dress things are a pain. I never know what to go as.
LAURA	It's so hard to find a good costume without spending a lot.
MATT	Yeah, but this mate of mine owns a warehouse. Stacks of theatre costumes stored there! He's lent me the key, so I'm going along to have a look when I get off duty.
AMY	All right for you, then!

MATT	You can borrow costumes too, if you want.
	[Ad lib responses, eg 'Really?' 'Brilliant' 'Thanks MATT' etc.]
	Let's meet in the car park, about six?
JOSH	Right, see you then.
	[LAURA & MATT exit. AMY notices JAKE, still sitting silently. She silently indicates Jake to JOSH with a nod of her head and pointed thumb, and they approach JAKE.]
	You O.K., son?
	[Jake nods, but doesn't look directly at the two adults]
AMY	Sure there's no problem?
JAKE	*(unconvincing)* Yeah... I'm all right.
JOSH	You know we're here to help, don't you?
	[JAKE looks up at him, about to blurt out his troubles, but he changes his mind and gets up.]
JAKE	*(glum)* Yeah, sure, but like I said, I'm fine, just waiting for a mate.
	[Enter children, including ANT, who approaches JAKE.]
JAKE	*(relieved, points to Ant)* That's him. *(waving)* Hey, Ant!
AMY	Right. Well, don't forget – we're there if you need us.
	[They exit, talking quietly to each other about the party.]
ANT	Hey, Jake, what did <u>they</u> want?
CHILD 1	You robbed a bank or something?
	[The children laugh, but JAKE doesn't respond.]
CHILD 2	What's the matter?
JAKE	It's those girls. You know, Ant, the ones you ran away from just now?
ANT	Yeah? What did they do?
JAKE	One of them nicked my mobile.
CHILDREN	*(shocked)* No!
ANT	D'you know who they were?
JAKE	Yeah, one of them was Ruby – you know – in Kim's gang.

CHILD 3	You should've punched them!
CHILD 4	Give 'em a hard time... like they give us.
ANT	Some chance!
JAKE	They're bigger than us.
CHILD 1	And stronger!
CHILD 2	I wish I had superhuman strength, I'd... I'd...
CHORUS L.	Bash 'em.
CHORUS R.	Chuck 'em in the pond!
ANT	*(doing strong man gesture with arms and fists)* Like Popeye!
CHILD 1	Nah! I hate spinach.
CHILD 2	Superman, then.
JAKE	*(laughing)* With your underpants over your trousers?
CHILDREN	Yeah!
	[Children laugh.]
CHILD 3	Leaping over the school in a single bound!
	[CHILD 3 does a run-up and a big leap]
CHILDREN	*(as CHILD 3 leaps)* Woah!
CHILD 3	And back again!
CHILDREN	*(as CHILD 3 leaps)* Woah!
JAKE	*(laughing at CHILD 3)* <u>You</u> wish!
CHILD 2	If only we could be like Superman...
CHILD 1	Yeah, really big and tough!
CHILDREN	Then they'd leave us alone!

[Extra children from the chorus could be featured during this number, eg. as the backing group.]

REAL TOUGH STUFF   (⊙ Track 3 / 18)

Jake   I COULD PLAY THE BIG GUY
WITH MUSCLES LIKE POPEYE.
I COULD BE A WINNER!

THEY WOULDN'T MESS WITH ME,
THEY WOULDN'T TAUNT AND TEASE
IF I ATE SPINACH FOR DINNER.
I'D BE REAL TOUGH STUFF,
YEAH, REAL TOUGH STUFF.
          Backing group: 'REAL TOUGH STUFF!'

Children and Chorus   NEED TO GET SOME BULK
LIKE INCREDIBLE HULK:
YOU COULD MAKE THEM SHIVER.

Jake   I COULD BE SCARY AN' GREEN,
I COULD BE UGLY AN' MEAN,

Children and Chorus   THAT WOULD MAKE THEM QUIVER.
YOU'D BE REAL TOUGH STUFF,
YEAH, REAL TOUGH STUFF.
          Backing group: 'REAL TOUGH STUFF!'

ALL   HE'S NO MATCH FOR MIGHTY KING KONG,
BODY-BUILDING COULD MAKE HIM LOOK STRONG!
WOAH – OH – OH – OH,

HE COULD PLAY THE BIG GUY
WITH MUSCLES LIKE POPEYE.
HE COULD BE A WINNER!
THEY WOULDN'T MESS WITH HIM,
THEY WOULDN'T TAUNT AND TEASE
IF HE ATE SPINACH FOR DINNER.
HE'D BE REAL TOUGH STUFF,
YEAH, REAL TOUGH STUFF.
          Backing group: 'REAL TOUGH STUFF!'

Jake   *(spoken sadly)*   I NEED MUSCLES BIG ENOUGH
AND A VOICE THAT'S GRUFF
TO GIVE THE RIGHT IMPRESSION.   *(sigh)*
I'M NO PIECE OF FLUFF,
THIS AIN'T JUST A BLUFF,
I'M A BUNDLE OF AGGRESSION.
(sung)   YES, I'M REAL TOUGH STUFF,
(spoken with a sigh)   REAL TOUGH STUFF.

ALL   WOAH – OH – OH – OH,
HE COULD PLAY THE BIG GUY
WITH MUSCLES LIKE POPEYE.
HE COULD BE A WINNER!

Jake   THEY WOULDN'T MESS WITH ME,
THEY WOULDN'T TAUNT AND TEASE

ALL   IF HE ATE SPINACH FOR DINNER.
HE'D BE REAL TOUGH STUFF,
YEAH, REAL TOUGH STUFF.
          ALL shout: 'REAL TOUGH STUFF!'

          *[To get a laugh, after the applause the high backing group could
          sing one more 'Real tough stuff!'   Then all except Child 1,2,3,4,
          Jake and Ant exit. As they leave, ELLIE & RUBY pass by,
          jeering.]*

RUBY	*(to JAKE)* Nah, nah, na-nah, nah!
ELLIE	*(nastily)* Loser!

[Exit RUBY & ELLIE]

JAKE	*(sighing)* Trouble is, it's not <u>muscles</u> you need with people like Kim.
ANT	How d'you mean?
JAKE	Well, people like Kim don't actually <u>hit</u> you. They just...
CHILD 1	Threaten you?

[JAKE nods.]

CHILD 2	They make you feel... scared... and sort of...
CHILD 3	Small?
CHILD 2	Yeah.

[Short pause.]

JAKE	If I was stronger I wouldn't be so scared.
CHILD 4	None of us would be scared if we were strong...

[Short pause, as all look glum]

ANT	*(sigh)* Oh well...
CHILD 3	See you next week, then...

[All exit sadly to incidental music.]

SAD STUFF (incidental)　　(⊙ Track 4 / 19)

SCENE 3　　　Ellie's house

The scene can be indicated by a table and chair brought on by props assistants. Enter ELLIE carrying a schoolbook. Enter ELLIE's MUM and DAD wearing coats, ready to go out. ELLIE looks miserable.

ELLIE	Do you have to go out tonight, Mum?
ELLIE's MUM	We always go out on Fridays, Ellie.
ELLIE	I know...
ELLIE's MUM	We won't be late back.
ELLIE	*(sadly)* Ok...
ELLIE's DAD	Make sure you do your homework.

ELLIE	(bored tone) Yes, Dad.
ELLIE's DAD	(turning to go) Rachel's here, so you don't need to worry.
ELLIE's MUM	(on her way out) She'll look after you.
ELLIE	(darkly, to herself) I <u>bet</u> she will!
ELLIE's DAD	(fiddling in his pocket) Hang on, where are the car keys?
ELLIE's MUM	(as they leave) It's ok, I've got them.

> [Exit ELLIE's MUM and DAD. As ELLIE settles down at the table reading her book, RACHEL enters & goes to ELLIE.]

RACHEL	(sarcastically, as she moves towards ELLIE) Still up, baby?

> [RACHEL swipes the book, waves it around out of ELLIE's reach.]

ELLIE	(trying to get her book back) Hey, Rachel! That's a school book.

> [RACHEL chucks the book across the room.]

RACHEL	Oh <u>dear</u>! Anyway, I'm watching TV, so you can go to bed!
ELLIE	(whining as she goes to pick up the book) But this is homework!
RACHEL	Tough! Anyway, look at your disgusting hair! Forget homework - you're better off studying hairdressing.
ELLIE	What's wrong with my hair?
RACHEL	(sneering) What's <u>right</u> with it? And your clothes! Yuk! Study fashion if you don't wanna look like a <u>loser</u>.
ELLIE	You're always so mean.
RACHEL	(mocking) You're always so mean! Go to bed, you baby.
ELLIE	But Rachel, it's only 8 o'clock!
RACHEL	(baby voice) Bedtime for babies, sleepy Ellie. (Sharply, pointing) Go!
ELLIE	(miserably, as she slouches off) Oh...

TOUGH STUFF (incidental)   (⊙ Track 5 / 20)

> [RACHEL sneers, hands on hips, watching as ELLIE goes, then laughs nastily and exits. Props assistants take off props.]

SCENE 4   Jake's money is stolen

Enter KIM, FRANKIE & gang, laughing and talking noisily.

KIM	.......and I hadn't done my homework, so I made that girl Jodie show me hers! *(Laughs)* Then I copied it and threw it away. Now she'll be handing it in late!

[All laugh nastily]

FRANKIE	Nice one!
GIRL 1	Why do homework when someone else can do it for you?
KIM	Exactly.
GIRL 2	That Jodie's such a loner.
GIRL 3	Yeah, and have you seen her clothes?
GIRL 4	What a mess!

[More scornful laughter]

KIM	Come on, let's go down the park.

[As they start to go JAKE enters, carrying a backpack. ELLIE sees him and whispers to RUBY. They stay as the others exit noisily, and move towards JAKE.]

ELLIE	*(pointing to JAKE)* There's that boy!
RUBY	*(moving to JAKE)* Hey, loser! Made any good phone calls lately?
ELLIE	Used up all your credit?

[RUBY & ELLIE are either side of JAKE doing a 'double act' as they tease and torment him. JAKE stands silently.]

RUBY	Never mind, Mumsy will get you another phone if you're a good boy!
ELLIE	Got any cash?

[JAKE shakes his head]

RUBY	Bet he has.
ELLIE	Come on, hand it over. I'm broke.

[ELLIE holds her hand out flat, palm up straight under his face. JAKE flinches but shakes his head.]

JAKE	No! Leave me alone!
RUBY	I'll hold him, you search his pockets.

[RUBY grabs his arms behind him and ELLIE scrabbles in JAKE's pockets as he struggles. She pulls out some coins.]

ELLIE	Great! Ice creams are on me, come on!

[They exit, laughing, RUBY speaking over her shoulder:]

RUBY	Hey, kid! Why don't you ring 999 – on your mobile!

[They laugh nastily as they leave. JAKE looks miserable. He hangs his head and scuffs his feet during the intro.]

MAKE TIME GO BACKWARDS   (⊙ Track 6 / 21)

Jake   WHAT CAN I DO? I NEED ADVICE.
I DON'T KNOW HOW TO CHANGE THINGS.
WHAT CAN I DO? WON'T SOMEONE BE NICE,
AND HELP ME REARRANGE THINGS?
WITH EACH DAY THAT COMES
I JUST FEEL MORE GLUM.
WISH I COULD...

MAKE TIME GO BACKWARDS,
MAKE TIME GO BACKWARDS.
REWIND THE DAYS,
TAKE THEM ALL AWAY.
(repeat)

[JAKE sits on ground in the centre, head in hands, fed up.]

ALL   HOW CAN HE TAKE THE SMALLEST STEP?
HE'S FRIGHTENED OF TOMORROW.
HOW CAN HE BREAK THIS PATTERN OF FEAR
WHEN HE'S EXPECTING SORROW?
WITH EACH DAY THAT COMES
HE JUST FEELS MORE GLUM.
WISH HE COULD...

MAKE TIME GO BACKWARDS ...   *(repeat)*

HE NEEDS A FRIEND TO TAKE HIS HAND,
A FRIEND WHO'LL GENTLY GUIDE HIM.
HE NEEDS SOMEONE TO HELP HIM STAND,
A FRIEND TO BE BESIDE HIM...

MAKE TIME GO FORWARDS,
MAKE TIME GO FORWARDS.
BRING ON THE DAY
A FRIEND WILL COME HIS WAY.
(repeat)
BRING ON THE DAY
A FRIEND WILL COME HIS WAY.

[DANNY enters from the opposite side of the stage, wearing a backpack. He goes up to JAKE.]

DANNY	Hiya! Haven't seen you for ages.

JAKE	*(without enthusiasm)* Hi.
DANNY	*(sitting down next to him)* Hey, I've got a couple of new jokes! Listen: What looks like an elephant and flies?
JAKE	*(drearily)* I dunno. What looks like an elephant and flies?
DANNY	A flying elephant! *(laughs)* Ok, not funny? Well... What about this one. Why can't a bicycle stand by itself?
JAKE	*(sighs)* I don't know. Why can't a bicycle stand by itself?
DANNY	Because it's two <u>tired</u>! *(Nudges JAKE to try and make him laugh.)* Geddit? Too tired!! *(making circles in the air to indicate the tyres)* Two tyres? Oh Jake! What's up?
JAKE	What's it to you?
DANNY	Maybe I can help.
JAKE	I doubt it.
DANNY	Nothing's that bad!
JAKE	Huh! If you went to my school you'd know...
DANNY	Know what?
JAKE	About this gang.
DANNY	A gang? What do they do?
JAKE	Oh, nick our stuff, spoil things, treat us like dirt..... you know....
DANNY	Uh... bullying stuff.
JAKE	Yeah. I'm sick of it, gonna run away.
DANNY	Run away? Cool! Not for ever, though?
JAKE	Nah. I just need a break.
DANNY	Excellent! But what about your Mum and Dad?
JAKE	*(fed up)* Huh! They're too busy to notice.
DANNY	Oh... I know a really good place to hide out.
JAKE	Where?
DANNY	*(getting up)* I'll show you.
JAKE	What, now?
DANNY	Why not? They'd never find us.

JAKE	*(undecided)* Well... *(almost decided)* O.K. ... *(nods, decided)* Yeah!
DANNY	Great! Let's do it!

[They exit, talking excitedly]

SCENE 5   In the street, Saturday. Danny's missing.

As many children as possible should be choreographed to move around to create a busy street feel.
POLICE officers can be included. GANG enter, including ELLIE, but not KIM.

SATURDAY   (☉ Track 7 / 22)

Chorus Part 1

SATURDAY, IN TOWN ON
SATURDAY. COME DOWN ON
SATURDAY. WE'RE HANGIN' ROUND
SO BE THERE.
SATURDAY, IN TOWN ON
SATURDAY. COME DOWN ON
SATURDAY. WE'RE HANGIN' ROUND.
JUST BE THERE:

Chorus

Part 1 & Part 2 in harmony
SATURDAY – IN TOWN ON
SATURDAY – COME DOWN ON
SATURDAY – WE'RE HANGIN' ROUND
SO BE THERE.
SATURDAY – IN TOWN ON
SATURDAY – COME DOWN ON
SATURDAY – WE'RE HANGIN' ROUND.

Gang   **& Chorus Part 1**   *(& CHORUS PART 2)*
                                    (WAH, WAH, WAH, OOO)
WE LOVE SATURDAY.   *(SATURDAY)*
SATURDAY *THERE'S NO SCHOOL.*
                        (WAH, WAH, WAH, OOO)
WE LOVE SATURDAY.   *(SATURDAY)*
SATURDAY *IS COOL.*
                        (WAH, WAH, WAH, OOO)
WE LOVE SATURDAY.   *(SATURDAY)*
SATURDAY *WE DON'T FUSS.*
                        (WAH, WAH, WAH, OOO)
WE LOVE SATURDAY.   *(SATURDAY)*
THAT'S THE DAY *FOR US.*
                        (WAH, WAH, WAH, OOO)

CHILD 1, 2 & 3 move to front of stage →

DIALOGUE :

Child 1	*(to CHILD 2 / 3)* Hey, it's Kim's gang! They took Jake's phone.
Child 2	Kim's not there! Let's see if we can get it back.
Child 3	You've got to be joking!
Child 2	*(shrugs, then walks to FRANKIE)* Um...I think one of you... borrowed my friend's phone? Could we have it back please?
Frankie	Get lost!
Child 1	Please... he really needs it.

Frankie	Don't know what you're talking about.
Child 2	I think you <u>do</u> know about it!
Frankie	Do you wanna kicking?
Child 3	No! He doesn't! *(to CHILD 2)* Come on – let's go!
Gang / Chorus	*(aggressively)* THIS PART OF TOWN IS NOT FOR YOU! IT'S NOT FOR YOU! YOU'D BETTER GET BACK TO WHERE YOU BELONG 'COS THIS PART OF TOWN IS NOT FOR YOU! GO HOME!

RUBY	*(shouting after them)* Go on, get lost!
ELLIE	*(laughing)* Huh! Idiots!
FRANKIE	Where's Kim?
GIRL 1	Dunno.
GIRL 2	Late again!
GIRL 3	*(pointing)* There she is!
	[KIM enters, seeming upset, lacking the usual bravado.]
ELLIE	C'mon, Kim, we'll miss the movie.
	[KIM shakes her head.]
KIM	I'm not bothered. I've got a problem.
RUBY	What's the matter?
KIM	It's my brother.
GIRL 4	*(laughing)* Yeah, <u>that's</u> a problem!
KIM	Shut up! He's gone missing if you want to know.
	[Gang members look a little worried]
GIRL 1	Gone missing?
KIM	Yeah. He was meant to meet my mum at 1 o'clock, but he never showed up. She's off her head worrying about him.
RUBY	Kids! What a pain!
KIM	He may be a pain, but he's still my brother. Mum's crying her eyes out, 'cos he's not even answering his phone.
GIRL 2	Has she rung the police?
	[KIM nods, looking on the edge of tears.]

GIRL 3	Whoa, this is serious stuff.
	[Small silence.]
ELLIE	We'll help you look, Kim.
GANG	*(together, ad lib)* Yeah! We'll help you! Come on! ...etc.
FRANKIE	He can't have gone far.
ELLIE	It'll be fun, like a treasure hunt! *(realising her tactlessness)* Sort of...

> Start CD Track 8 /23 here

KIM	*(speaking over music)* He's only a kid... It's scary out there.....

OUT THERE   (☉ Track 8 / 23)

Kim
UNTIL TODAY
I THOUGHT I REALLY DIDN'T CARE.
UNTIL TODAY
I THOUGHT DANNY WOULD ALWAYS BE THERE.
AND NOW HE'S GONE
I KNOW THAT NOTHING IS THE SAME,
AND NOW HE'S GONE
I KNOW SOMEHOW THAT I AM TO BLAME.
FOR ONCE I CAN SAY
I REALLY DON'T KNOW WHAT TO DO.

ALL
OUT THERE IT'S LONELY.
OUT THERE YOU'RE ON YOUR OWN.
IT'S DARK, IT'S COLD,
AND NO-ONE KNOWS YOUR NAME
OUT THERE. IT'S SCARY.
YOU COULD DROP LIKE A STONE,
FALLING FLAT TO THE GROUND,
PEOPLE PASSING BY
WOULDN'T EVEN LOOK DOWN.
YOU'D HAVE TO BE BRAVE
UNTIL SOMEONE SAVED YOU OUT THERE.

Kim
THE STREET IS DARK.
MAYBE THERE'S NO-ONE BY HIS SIDE.
THE STREET IS DARK.
NIGHT SURROUNDS HIM WHEREVER HE HIDES.
IS HE ALIVE?
OH HOW I WISH THINGS HADN'T CHANGED.
IS HE ALIVE?
OR WILL I BE FOREVER TO BLAME?

ALL
FOR ONCE WE CAN SAY
WE REALLY DON'T KNOW WHAT TO DO.

OUT THERE IT'S LONELY... ETC.

.... YOU'D HAVE TO BE BRAVE
UNTIL SOMEONE SAVED YOU
OUT THERE.

> *[At the end of the song the gang exit in silence, RUBY could put her arm round KIM. During incidental music, props assistants place some large boxes – containing costumes – upstage.]*

OUT THERE *(fade when ready)*　**(⊙ Track 23)**

SCENE 6　　　　In the warehouse

JAKE & DANNY enter with rucksacks, and drinking from bottles of water.

JAKE	Are we nearly there?
DANNY	Very nearly there.
JAKE	*(tired)*　How far, though?
DANNY	*(sarcastically, pointing at the 'warehouse')*　Think you can make it across the street?
JAKE	Thank goodness!　My legs hurt!
	DANNY & JAKE stand downstage, as if in street outside the warehouse.　They finish their water as they watch a MOTHER, FATHER, SON & DAUGHTER walk by, chatting.]
DAUGHTER	That movie was excellent!
SON	Yeah, thanks Mum!
MOTHER	That's ok.　I enjoyed it too.
FATHER	It was nice to go out as a family.　We should do it more often.
MOTHER	Yes, we should.
FATHER	How about a pizza?
SON /DAUGHTER	Yes please!
FATHER	OK, let's go!
	[MOTHER, FATHER, SON & DAUGHTER exit cheerfully, talking ad lib about pizza toppings. JAKE & DANNY watch them go.]
JAKE	*(sighing)*　All right for some.

	[They put their bottles back in their backpacks, then DANNY leads the way upstage to the warehouse area, and could climb in over a stage block or past a screen]
JAKE	*(looking around)* Wow! What's this, some sort of warehouse?
DANNY	Yeah.
JAKE	*(impressed)* Nobody will find us here!
	[JAKE settles down on a large box or similar.]
DANNY	Jake, I was wondering... Why don't you tell your Mum about that gang?
JAKE	What, tell her I'm being bullied? By a load of girls?
DANNY	*(laughing)* <u>Girls</u>? Big scary girlies?
JAKE	*(forcefully)* You wouldn't laugh if it was you.
DANNY	*(laughing more)* Hitting you with their handbags?
JAKE	*(jumps off the tea-chest, upset and angry)* Stop it! It's not like that! They're horrible!
	[JAKE turns his back and walks away to stand facing the audience, looking angry.]
DANNY	*(trying to stop laughing)* Sorry, but it's a funny thought!
	[JAKE stays silent and folds his arms.]
	(seriously, after a pause) Seriously, shouldn't you tell your mum about the bullying?
JAKE	*(sadly, walking back to DANNY)* No. She's always too busy. She never has time to listen.
DANNY	Oh... Still, I bet she's wondering where you are.
JAKE	*(sitting)* And your mum too.....
DANNY	I suppose... *(walks away)* Though she's more interested in... Oh, never mind.
JAKE	I'd ring home, but I don't have a phone, since those girls nicked it.
DANNY	*(moves to look out of the 'warehouse' area)* It'll be getting dark soon.
JAKE	*(worried)* We probably shouldn't have done this. Dad'll be <u>so</u> angry.
DANNY	Well, it's too late now.

[Incidental music is played 'under' the dialogue, to finish at the beginning of the next scene.]

BACKWARDS (incidental)   (☉ Track 9 / 24)

DANNY	*(yawning)* I'm really tired.
JAKE	Me too, but what if someone comes in here? We're trespassing, aren't we?
DANNY	Why would anyone come here at night? It'll be ok. *(pointing)* We could sleep over there.
JAKE	Yeah, I guess...

[They move between some boxes and sit down, taking their coats out of their backpacks to spread over themselves.]

DANNY	Not as cosy as a duvet, but it'll have to do.
JAKE	The floor's hard too...
DANNY	*(yawning)* Oh well – good night!
JAKE	Night.

[JAKE & DANNY settle down to sleep. When the music changes, MATT, LAURA, JOSH & AMY enter. Jake & Danny are alarmed, reacting with 'Shh!' gestures, etc., then watch what follows. Laura delivers her line just before incidental music fades.]

SCENE 7   **The dressing up scene**

LAURA	So where are the costumes?
MATT	In these boxes.
AMY	Can we really borrow anything we like?
MATT	*(proudly)* Yep. This mate likes to keep on my good side!
JOSH	*(mock impressed)* Ooh, Matt, you're so important!

[MATT pulls a face at him. AMY & LAURA giggle.]

MATT	Let's see what there is.

[They drag a couple of boxes from the side to centre, but do not see the two boys 'sleeping'. They examine the contents of the boxes. AMY pulls out a ballet dress.]

AMY	There you go Josh – just right for you!

[*The others all laugh. JOSH holds the costume in front of him and does a few very bad dance steps.*]

LAURA　　　　　Well maybe not!

AMY　　　　　Not exactly Swan Lake!

MATT　　　　　More like Duck Pond!

[*More laughter. LAURA pulls out a pop-star wig. She puts it on and drapes a piece of glamorous material around her shoulders, then does a slinky walk across the acting area.*]

LAURA　　　　　This is better. Who do I look like?

AMY　　　　　____ *(any well known girl singer)* ____　?　or maybe not!

MATT　　　　　Give us a song, Laura!

[*LAURA can launch into a rendition of any popular song in the charts at the time of performance*]

JOSH　　　　　She needs a backing group!

AMY　　　　　Come on!

[*They rummage in the box, chatting excitedly 'Look at this' etc. AMY & JOSH quickly put on some glamorous clothes & accessories to look like pop stars. They group as if round a microphone with LAURA and maybe do 'bop shoo wadda' sounds as she 'sings'.　This all needs to be playful and 'over the top'.*]

AMY　　　　　*(picking out a Charlie Chaplin style hat/stick and putting on the hat)*
Don't you wish you could be someone else now and again?

LAURA　　　　　That'd be fun, seeing through someone else's eyes.

SOMEONE ELSE'S EYES　　　(⊙ Track 10 / 25)

Amy　　I'D LIKE TO BE CHARLIE CHAPLIN FOR A WHILE
　　　　　TO MAKE YOU SMILE.

Laura　I'D LIKE TO BE CLEOPATRA FOR A DAY,
　　　　　GET MY OWN WAY!

Matt　　I'D LIKE TO BE SHERLOCK HOLMES FOR QUITE SOME TIME
　　　　　SOLVING CRIME.

Josh　　IN A DEERSTALKER HAT:　I'D FANCY THAT!

ALL　　SO JUST PRETEND YOU'RE IN THEIR SHOES!
　　　　　YOU CAN BE ANYONE YOU CHOOSE,
　　　　　TRY THEIR LIVES:　GO IN DISGUISE!

SEE THE WORLD
THROUGH SOMEONE ELSE'S EYES!

Laura	I'D LIKE TO BE QUEEN OF ENGLAND FOR A WHILE, AND LIVE IN STYLE.
Matt	I'D LIKE TO BE A FOOTBALL CAPTAIN FOR A DAY, GET LOTS OF PAY!
Josh	I'D LIKE TO BE ARISTOTLE FOR A WEEK, BEING GREEK.
Amy	MATHEMATICS ON A PLATE: THAT WOULD BE GREAT!
ALL	SO JUST PRETEND... *(etc.)*

YOU MIGHT DRESS IN RAGS,
YOU MIGHT DRESS IN ROBES.
ALL THE SAME YOU'RE STILL JUST YOU:
THAT'S THE WAY IT GOES!

> *[During the rest of the song MATT, LAURA, JOSH & AMY pick the costumes they are definitely keeping, and put the rest away.]*

YOU COULD BE SOMEONE FIERCE LIKE CAPTAIN HOOK,
A NASTY CROOK!
OR YOU COULD BE SOMEONE BRAVE LIKE ROBIN HOOD,
AND FIGHT FOR GOOD!
YOU COULD BE A SUPERHERO WITH SUCH MIGHT:
WHAT A SIGHT!
SOARING UP TO THE STARS ñ YOU'D FLY TO MARS!

SO JUST PRETEND...
....SEE THE WORLD THROUGH SOMEONE ELSE'S EYES!
SEE THE WORLD THROUGH SOMEONE ELSE'S EYES!

AMY   How do I look?

MATT   *(ironically, as she's in a silly outfit)* A great improvement, Amy!

AMY   Huh! Thanks a lot!

> *[LAURA is nearest to JAKE & DANNY's hiding place. Suddenly DANNY can't help coughing. It is not a loud cough, and only LAURA hears it, but DANNY claps his hands over his mouth. The boys look scared at the thought of being discovered and shrink further behind the boxes.]*

LAURA   *(turning suddenly, alarmed)* What was that?

JOSH   What?

AMY   I didn't hear anything.

MATT   *(mock frightened)* Ooh, Laura! It's the phantom of the warehouse!

LAURA   Oh stop it!

JOSH	*(wobbly spooky voice)* Oh no.....! A petrifying poltergeist!
LAURA	No, really! Over there! (pointing in JAKE & DANNY'S direction)
	[Pause, as all four listen for a moment until JOSH leans towards LAURA without her seeing him.]
JOSH	*(shouting just behind LAURA)* Boo!
LAURA	*(gives a little scream)* Oh, Josh! DON'T!
	[JOSH, AMY & MATT laugh at her]
	But I did hear something...... *(She looks around nervously)* It sounded like a cough!
AMY	A cough?
	[MATT coughs behind his hand, so that LAURA can't see]
	Oh it's only Matt.
LAURA	Yeah, that one was, maybe, but the one I heard was over there.
	[JOSH coughs dramatically behind her and falls noisily to the floor, twitching as if in death throes. LAURA gives a startled little scream.]
	Oh Josh, you idiot!
MATT	She's such a brave police officer, don't you think?
JOSH	Yeah, it's all that expensive training she's had!
AMY	*(businesslike)* Maybe Laura DID hear something. We should have a proper look around.
	[MATT, JOSH & AMY take a quick look around, but before they get to the boys' boxes JOSH looks at his watch.]
JOSH	Actually, it's time we went, or we'll be late for the party.
LAURA	*(rather resentfully)* Good, let's go!
AMY	*(to LAURA)* Anyway, at least we've got some great costumes.
	[The four exit, taking their chosen costumes with them. MATT & JOSH chatting and laughing together, AMY trying to cheer LAURA up. Slight pause as JAKE & DANNY peer cautiously round the boxes before emerging.]
JAKE	That was close. Good job they didn't spot us.
	[JAKE follows in the direction the police officers went for a moment, then returns in response to Danny's next line.]

DANNY   Yes. Let's try and get to sleep. *(Both lie down)*

                            [JAKE moves restlessly during the song, unable to settle]

OUT THERE (reprise)　　(☉ Track 11 / 26)

ALL   OUT THERE IT'S LONELY.
OUT THERE YOU'RE ON YOUR OWN.
IT'S DARK, IT'S COLD,
AND NO-ONE KNOWS YOUR NAME
OUT THERE. IT'S SCARY.
YOU COULD DROP LIKE A STONE,
FALLING FLAT TO THE GROUND,
PEOPLE PASSING BY
WOULDN'T EVEN LOOK DOWN.
YOU'D HAVE TO BE BRAVE
UNTIL SOMEONE SAVED YOU OUT THERE.
                  (repeat last 2 lines)

JAKE   *(sitting up and speaking over the music)*   I wonder if anyone is looking for us...

                            [DANNY doesn't respond]

Danny, are you awake?   *(disappointed)* ...oh...

                            [rubs his eyes, looking tearful]

(small voice) Good night, Mum...   Good night, Dad...

                            [JAKE begins to cry, lies down again, then settles to sleep.]

SCENE 8　　　The Warehouse, early next day

MORNING   (incidental)　　(☉ Track 12 / 27)

                          [DANNY & JAKE stretch and wake.]

DANNY   Ugh! That floor was hard!

JAKE   Yes. I hardly slept a wink, and I'm so hungry...

DANNY   Me too.   *(Digs in his pocket)* Have you got any money?

JAKE   No. Those girls took it all, remember?

DANNY   Oh yeah. Hang on...   *(counting coins)* I've got enough for some bread. Wait here.

                          [JAKE snuggles back down as if to sleep, face hidden. DANNY leaves the 'warehouse', moving into the street area. KIM enters, followed by GANG. Seeing Danny she rushes to him.]

KIM	*(amazed & relieved)* It's him! Danny! Are you OK?
DANNY	Kim? What are you doing here?
KIM	*(angry)* Looking for you, stupid! Where have you been? We've been so worried!
	[She turns to the gang members]
	One of you – run back to my house.....tell Mum and Dad he's safe.
	[GIRL 1 nods and exits quickly]
RUBY	Why did you run away?
KIM	Did someone upset you?
DANNY	No... I was helping a friend.
KIM	*(suspiciously)* What friend? What've you been up to?
DANNY	Nothing. He's being bullied.
GIRL 2	Where is he then?
KIM	And why did <u>you</u> have to help him?
DANNY	He needed a friend. You should hear some of the things he told me.
GIRL 3	Poor kid. Lucky he's got a friend like you Danny.
GIRL 2	But running away is a bit risky.
GIRL 3	Yeah. Couldn't he have stayed at your house?
KIM	Yes! You should have told me.
FRANKIE	We'd have sorted those bullies out.
ALL GANG	Yeah!
DANNY	They even took his mobile phone. He can't get another one 'cos his Mum's got no money. He only had it for emergencies.
	[PAUSE as the girls look at each other. ELLIE & RUBY move to one side, looking embarrassed as the truth hits them.]
KIM	*(quietly)* Come on Dan, let's go meet your friend.
DANNY	*(unaware of the changed atmosphere)* Yeah! Sure!
	[DANNY leads KIM into the warehouse. Other gang members follow, including ELLIE and RUBY, but they hang back to one side, mouthing 'What shall we do?' etc. JAKE is lying down.]
	Jake, wake up! They've found us.

JAKE	(sleepily) Who's found us?
DANNY	My sister and her friends.

[JAKE sits up, takes in GANG. He stands slowly, looking scared.]

JAKE	(to Danny) But Danny, it was them!
DANNY	Who?
JAKE	(indicating Ruby and Ellie) They took my phone!
DANNY	(astonished) What? (crossing to the girls) Why did you do that?
ELLIE	(pointing to Kim) She told me to.
DANNY	Kim told you? (turning back to KIM) Are these your friends? What's going on?

[There is a pause. Everyone looks uncomfortable.]

RUBY	Ellie wanted to join the gang.
DANNY	Whose gang?
KIM	(ashamed, after a pause) Mine.
DANNY	So you're in charge? Of these... bullies?

[KIM hangs her head, scuffing her feet.]

I can't believe my own sister's a bully. Why, Kim?
Why d'you have to do it?

[Those on stage mutter to each other ad lib during the intro. DANNY turns away in disgust, moves upstage with his back to the action. JAKE sits with his back to the audience, listening until he joins in with the chorus on 'So you turned into...']

BULLY!   (⊙ Track 13 / 28)

Chorus	WHAT TURNED YOU INTO A BULLY?
	HOW DID YOU GET TO BE COLDER THAN ICE?
	WHAT TURNED YOU INTO A BULLY?
	WHAT STOPPED YOU BEING NICE?
	BULLY! WHY D'YOU DO IT?

DANNY moves to
listen to KIM.

Kim	SINCE I STARTED SCHOOL AT FIVE
	PEOPLE PICKED ON ME.
Chorus	Aah-aah-aah!
Kim	WHY SHOULD I BE NICE OR KIND?
	I WAS BULLIED, I HAD NO FRIENDS,
	WAS ALWAYS PUSHED AROUND.

DANNY moves
downstage to one side,
facing audience, arms
folded, looking miserable.

Gang	WE GOT HASSLED ALL THE TIME,
	'TIL WE MADE THE GANG.

WITH EACH OTHER WE'RE JUST FINE.
NO-ONE BOTHERS TO MESS WITH US
WHEN ALL THE GANG'S IN TOWN.

Chorus   SO YOU TURNED INTO A BULLY.   (*Group: BULLY!*)
HOW DOES IT FEEL TO BE COLDER THAN ICE?
SO YOU TURNED INTO A BULLY.   (*Group: BULLY!*)
NOW DO YOU THINK YOU'RE NICE?

THERE'S CHOICE IN EACH SITUATION.
YOU'VE ALWAYS CHOSEN TO GIVE OTHERS PAIN.
THERE'S CHOICE IN EACH SITUATION.
WHY DON'T YOU CHOOSE AGAIN?
BULLY! HERE'S YOUR CHOICE NOW!
BULLY! NICE OR NASTY?
BULLY! ------ NICE OR NASTY?

[PAUSE. KIM hangs her head in shame, scuffing her feet, hands in pockets.]

DANNY	I'm ashamed of my own sister...
JAKE	*(to DANNY)* But she might change now.
DANNY	Huh!
JAKE	Danny, she's your sister! You have to give her a chance.
DANNY	*(sarcastically)* Like she gave you a chance? Huh!
JAKE	Well, yeah, but weren't you listening? They said they're all bullies 'cos someone bullied them.
DANNY	*(grudgingly)* Mmm. *(to the gang in general)* Is that true?
GANG	*(ad lib)* Yes. That's right... etc.
ELLIE	What else can you do? You've got to stand up for yourself...
FRANKIE	*(moving downstage right)* There's always someone out to get you.
RUBY	*(moving to Frankie, thoughtfully)* Yes, but the gang makes us strong.
DANNY	But why does being strong mean you have to pick on other people?
KIM	We don't, unless they pick on us first.
DANNY	Kim – it was because of your gang that Jake ran away! It was your fault! And he wasn't picking on you. You lot just bullied him.
GIRL 1	Well it was Ellie who actually did it...

[All look at KIM]

KIM	*(resigned)* I suppose it was my fault. I gave her the challenge.

ELLIE	But I took his phone. *(Pause, before crossing to JAKE)* *(ashamed, as she hands back his phone)* Here. Sorry.
JAKE	*(with a shrug)* That's ok.
	[*ELLIE turns and starts to walk back to where she was.*]
	Hang on, though... Tell me... Who's picking on you?
ELLIE	*(turning around and speaking slowly, reluctantly)* Well... It's my big sister – Rachel. She's really mean. *(to Kim)* Even you'd be scared.
KIM	Really? Nothing much scares me. What does she do?
ELLIE	*(miserably)* She makes me feel small. Treats me like dirt.
KIM	Can't you stand up to her?
ELLIE	Not on my own.
RUBY	But what if there's a few of us?
FRANKIE	We could help.
KIM	We could go with you – and talk to her.
	[*GANG make noises of agreement, 'Let's go', etc.*]
	Will you come, Danny?
DANNY	Not if you're going to bully her as well. It'll never end!
	[*Thoughtful pause*]
KIM	(to Ellie) Perhaps we need to find out who's bullying your sister.
ELLIE	What, Rachel? D'you think she's being bullied?
JAKE	Yes! If this theory works, she's got to be a victim too.
ELLIE	But I know what Rachel's like... Who'd pick on her?
	[*All look uncertain for a moment*]
KIM	Well, you never know. (to Danny) You coming, then?
DANNY	Ok, let's go.
	[*All exit. 'BULLY' backing music may be used to cover this exit.*]

SCENE 9   Jake and Ellie confront Rachel

Enter Rachel.   She sits and fiddles with her shoe.   Enter KIM, ELLIE, JAKE, DANNY and GANG.
GANG hang back, as ELLIE & JAKE approach RACHEL.

ELLIE	*(nervously)* Rachel... um... I've got something to say.
RACHEL	What's he doing here?
JAKE	*(stepping forward)* Your sister's been bullying me.
RACHEL	*(nastily)* What, Ellie? A bully? Don't make me laugh!
	[*ELLIE puts her hands up to her face and turns away to cover her embarrassment.*]
JAKE	*(bolder)* Yes... She's a bully!
	[*RACHEL stands up*]
	And I want it to stop. Right now!
RACHEL	*(towers over JAKE menacingly)* Think you're Mr. Tough, do you? *(prods his chest)* You're just a shrimp! *(prods again)* Little shrimp!
	[*KIM and DANNY approach as RACHEL speaks, followed by the others, who stand spread well behind them.*]
ELLIE	Rachel! Don't!
JAKE	Stop it, Rachel! You don't frighten me!
RACHEL	*(grabbing his shirt)* Are you <u>sure</u> about that, little boy?
	[*Those in the background close in as KIM steps forward*]
KIM	Rachel! *(folding her arms)* He's not on his own.
	[*RACHEL, startled, drops JAKE's shirt.*]
RACHEL	*(looking around)* What's all this?
KIM	Ellie picked on Jake because you're always picking on her.
RACHEL	Says who?
KIM	Doesn't matter, does it? You know what the truth is.

WRONG AIN'T RIGHT   (☉ Track 14 / 29)

Ellie WHAT DO I DO THAT BOTHERS YOU?
YOU PICK ON ME NO MATTER WHAT I DO.
YOU BOSS ME ABOUT FROM MORNIN' TO NIGHT.
SEEMS YOU'RE ONLY HAPPY WHEN YOU PICK A FIGHT.

Chorus WRONG AIN'T RIGHT, OH NO,
DARK AIN'T LIGHT,
DON'T YA KNOW THAT
DAY AIN'T NIGHT.

GOTTA TELL YA THAT PUSHING, SHOVING,
MAKIN' HER CRY –
IT'S NOT ALL RIGHT,
I SAID IT'S NOT ALL RIGHT,
AND LIFE IS NOTHIN' BUT A FIGHT
IF YOU DON'T KNOW WRONG FROM RIGHT.

Jake AT THE END OF DAY, WHEN YOU GO TO BED,
WHAT KIND OF THOUGHTS ARE IN YOUR HEAD?
ARE YOU PLEASED WITH THE WAY YOU SPENT YOUR DAY,
OR MAYBE FEELIN' GUILTY 'BOUT THE THINGS YOU SAY?

Chorus WRONG AIN'T RIGHT... etc.

Ruby YOU TAUNT AND TEASE WITH NO REASON WHY.
ARE YOU PLEASED TO SEE YOUR SISTER CRY?
WHY LET WICKEDNESS GET INTO YOUR HEAD?
WOULDN'T IT BE BETTER TO BE FRIENDS INSTEAD?

Chorus WRONG AIN'T RIGHT... etc.

... NOTHIN' BUT A FIGHT
IF YOU DON'T KNOW WRONG FROM RIGHT.
NOTHIN' BUT A FIGHT
IF YOU DON'T KNOW WRONG FROM RIGHT.
THAT'S RIGHT!

[During the song RACHEL has the grace to look a little ashamed, and she loses her aggression. She sits down on the wall and looks depressed. There is an awkward pause. ELLIE scuffs her feet.]

KIM *(impatiently)* Well talk to her then, Ellie!

ELLIE *(nervously)* Rachel, why are you so horrible to me? I'm your sister!

RACHEL *(grumpily)* I know.

ELLIE You treat me like a baby. Put yourself in my shoes.
Would you like it?

DANNY Can't you try and see things through her eyes?

RACHEL I just feel so angry sometimes.

KIM Is someone picking on you?

RACHEL Not really.

[There is a pause. They all look at Rachel]

JAKE No-one picking on you? *(to DANNY)* Kind of ruins the theory...

ELLIE *(horrified)* So you're just being horrible? Just for... fun?

RACHEL I can't stop myself.

KIM	*(thoughtfully, to RACHEL)* I know what you mean… Sometimes I can't stop myself… *(walks to one side)*
DANNY	*(to RACHEL)* But you could try.
RACHEL	I <u>do</u> try.
JAKE	Try harder!
KIM	Yeah, we should both try harder. *(walks back to RACHEL)*

[Short awkward pause]

FRANKIE	*(trying to make light of things)* What's this? Don't tell me Kim's turning over a new leaf?
RUBY	Scary! How do people get in the gang if she's gone nice?
GIRL 1	I dunno! Do a thousand press-ups?

[GANG laugh – 'Yeah, right!' etc.]

GIRL 2	Give your worst enemy a hug?
ALL	Ugh!
GIRL 1 /2	*(open arms)* Give up chocolate?
ALL	*(horrified)* Never!
JAKE	Well if you gave up chocolate, at least you wouldn't nick mine!

[All laugh, except RACHEL]

RACHEL	It's all right for you. You've all got each other. Who have I got?
ELLIE	If you were nicer to me, we could be friends… sort of… maybe…

[RACHEL looks uncertain for a moment, folding her arms and chewing her lip, but then she starts crying, with her arm over her eyes. Children should be encouraged to take their time over this. ELLIE puts her arm around Rachel's shoulders and leaves it there during the next line.]

RACHEL	*(still crying into her arm)* I don't mean to treat you like a baby…
ELLIE	*(pulls away, flexing muscles)* I'm not a baby! Look at these muscles!
ALL	Look at those muscles!

[RACHEL laughs as she wipes her eyes.]

RACHEL	I'm sorry, Ellie.

[ELLIE leaves a short pause to let the apology sink in.]

ELLIE   That's ok, Rachel.

                 [*All watch as ELLIE & RACHEL do a <u>slow</u> high five, then hug.*]

JAKE   Being tough isn't just about having muscles...

RUBY   But it helps!

DANNY   Or does it?

ALL   *(to audience)* What do you think?

REAL TOUGH STUFF (reprise) (⊙ Track 15 / 30)

ALL   WE COULD PLAY THE BIG GUY
            WITH MUSCLES LIKE POPEYE.
            WE COULD ALL BE WINNERS!
            THEY WOULDN'T MESS WITH US,
            THEY WOULDN'T TAUNT AND TEASE
            IF WE ATE SPINACH FOR DINNER.
            WE'D BE REAL TOUGH STUFF,
            YEAH, REAL TOUGH STUFF.
                 Backing group: 'REAL TOUGH STUFF!'

            NEED TO GET SOME BULK
            LIKE INCREDIBLE HULK:
            WE COULD MAKE THEM SHIVER.
            WE COULD BE SCARY AN' GREEN,
            WE COULD BE UGLY AN' MEAN,
            THAT WOULD MAKE THEM QUIVER.
            WE'D BE REAL TOUGH STUFF,
            YEAH, REAL TOUGH STUFF.
                 Backing group: 'REAL TOUGH STUFF!'

            WE'RE NO MATCH FOR MIGHTY KING KONG,
            BODY-BUILDING COULD MAKE US LOOK STRONG!
            WOAH – OH – OH – OH,
            WE COULD PLAY THE BIG GUY
            WITH MUSCLES LIKE POPEYE.
            WE COULD ALL BE WINNERS!
            THEY WOULDN'T MESS WITH US,
            THEY WOULDN'T TAUNT AND TEASE
            IF WE ATE SPINACH FOR DINNER.
            WE'D BE REAL TOUGH STUFF,
            YEAH, REAL TOUGH STUFF.
                 ALL shout: 'REAL TOUGH STUFF!'

© 2006 Starshine Music Ltd.
Brown Cottage, Glynleigh Road, Hankham, East Sussex, England.
BN24 5BJ.   Tel: +44(0)1323 764334   Fax: +44(0)1323 767145
e-mail: info@starshine.co.uk

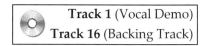
Track 1 (Vocal Demo)
Track 16 (Backing Track)

Where's Kim?

Music and Lyrics by Ruth Kenward
Arranged by Mark Dickman

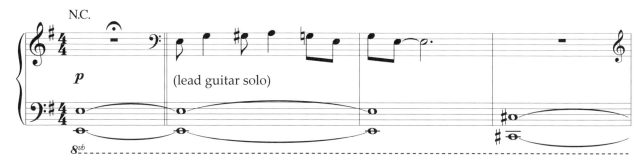

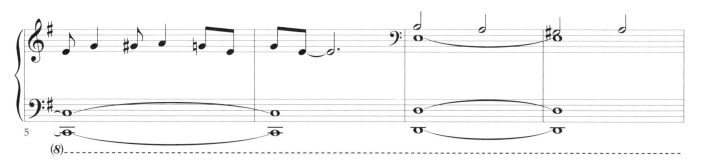

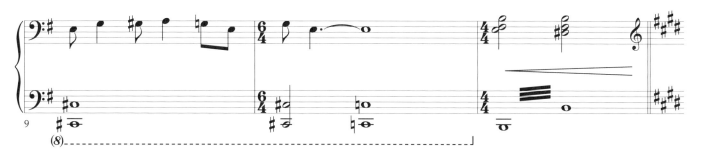

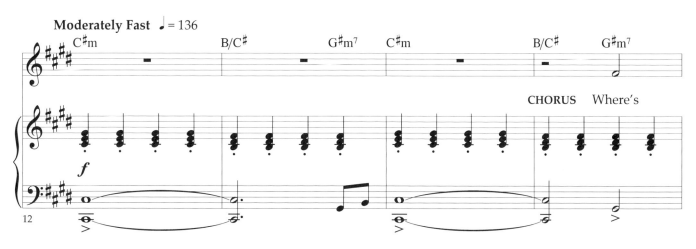

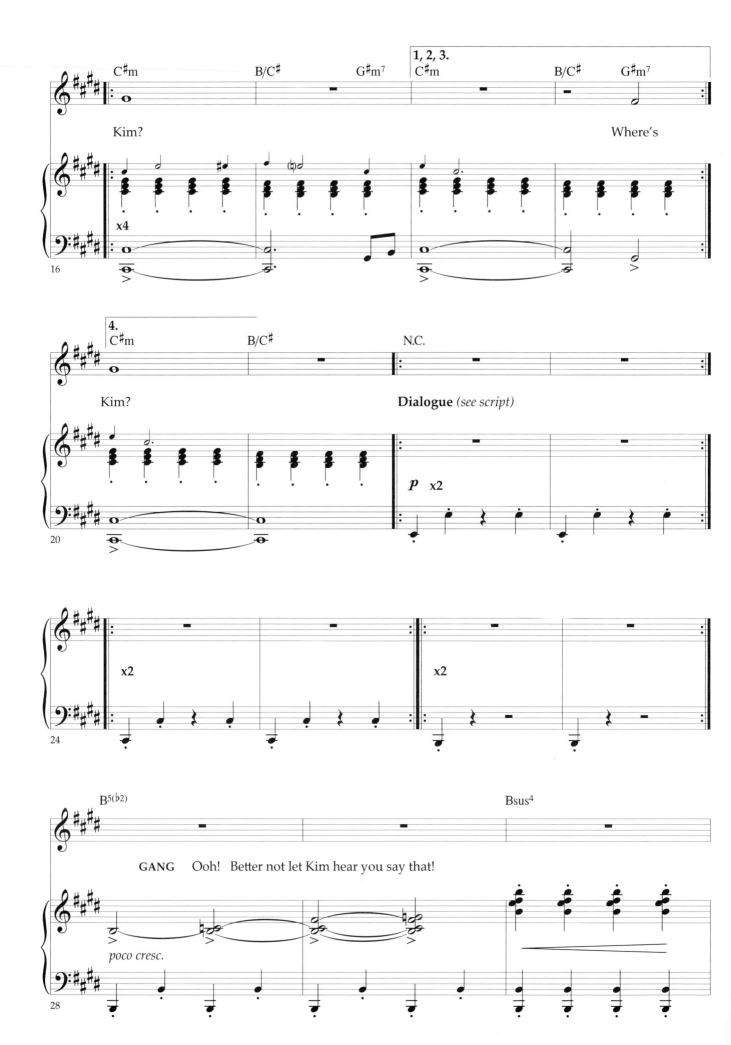

cross. **KIM** *(spoken) Oh come on, just tell me why!* **GIRL 2** There's this
cross. **GANG** Won't you let us tell you why? **KIM** *(spoken) Go on*

girl. **KIM** *(spoken) What a - bout her? What's her name?*
then... **GANG** She's Ru - by's friend and she's o - k.

GIRL 2 We let her in - to the gang. **KIM** *(spoken) In our*
KIM I say who gets in the gang.

CHORUS
She says who gets in the gang. **KIM** Who is she, anyway? **CHORUS 1** El - lie

41

know what I said, it's me makes the rules.

She'd bet - ter be good or

you'll look like fools. **KIM / FRANKIE** She must pass_ the

test, be as good as the rest.___ She

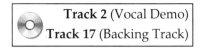
In The Gang

Music and Lyrics by Ruth Kenward

Arranged by Mark Dickman

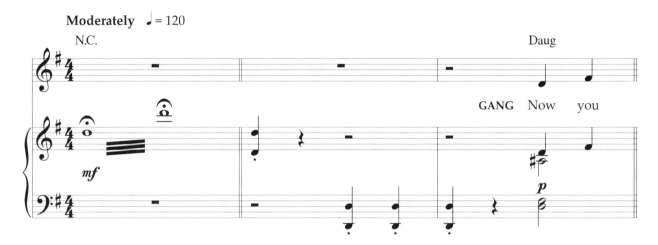

one of them, one of

them, one of them.

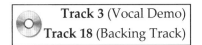
Real Tough Stuff

Music and Lyrics by Ruth Kenward
Arranged by Mark Dickman

50

Make Time Go Backwards

Music and Lyrics by Ruth Kenward
Arranged by Mark Dickman

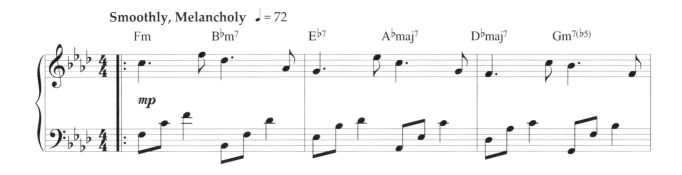

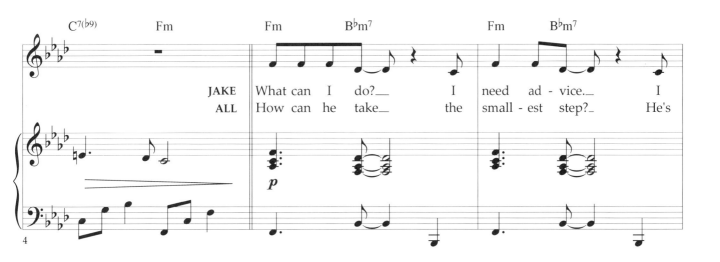

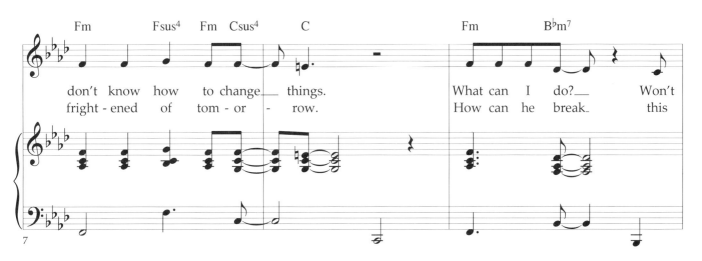

55

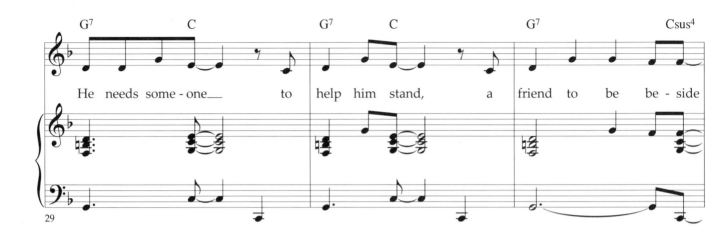

He needs some-one____ to help him stand, a friend to be be-side

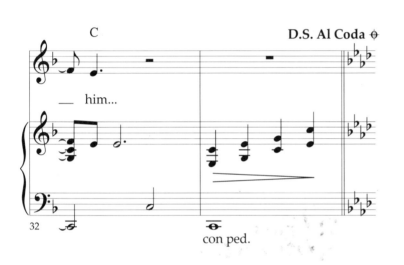

____ him...

D.S. Al Coda ⊕

con ped.

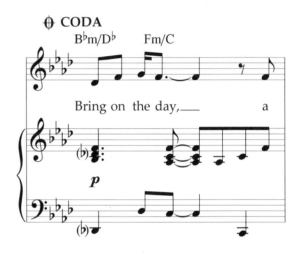

⊕ CODA

Bring on the day,____ a

friend will come his way.

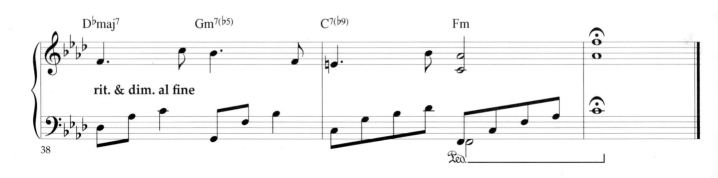

rit. & dim. al fine

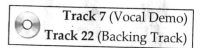
Saturday

Music and Lyrics by Ruth Kenward
Arranged by Mark Dickman

*(swung semiquavers)

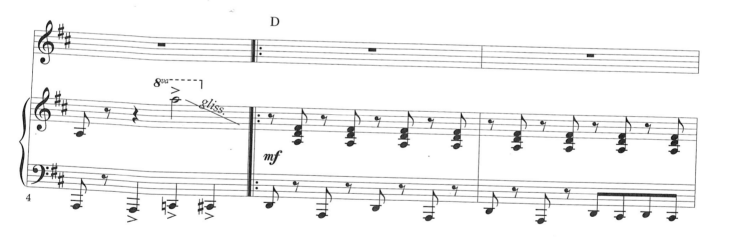

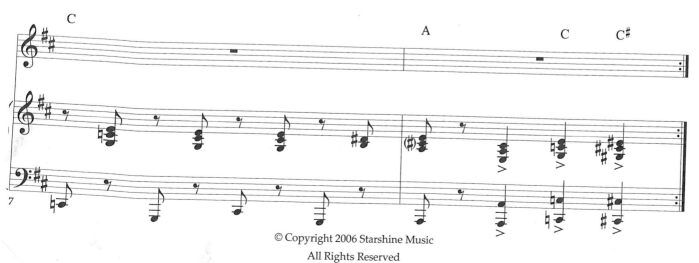

58

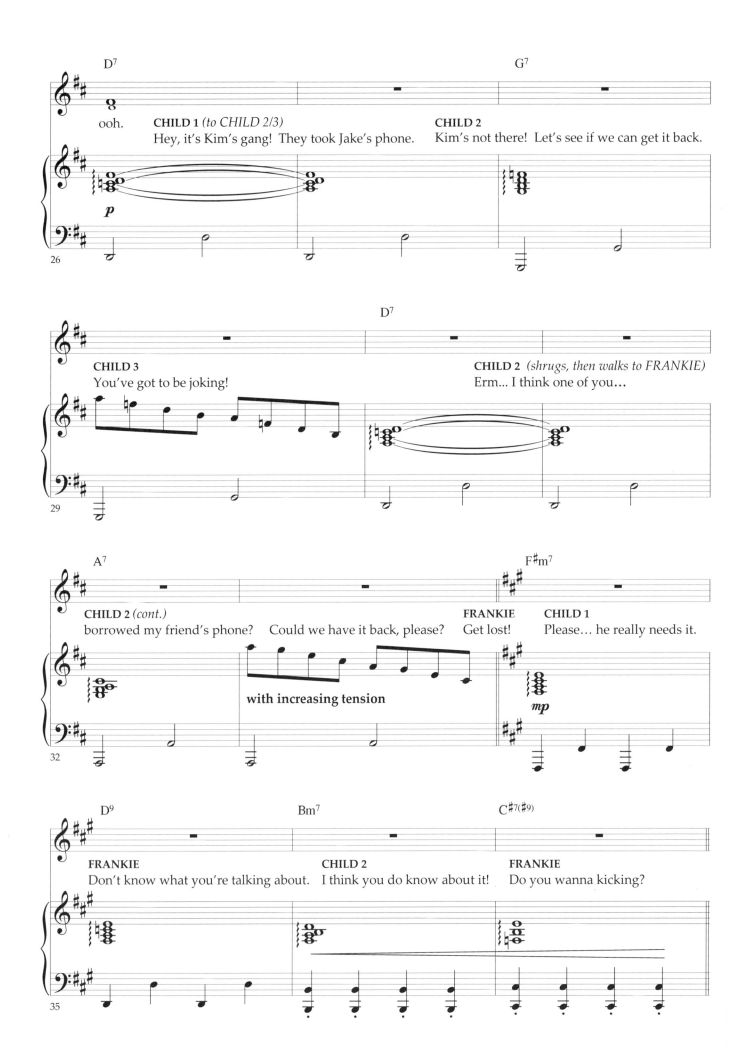

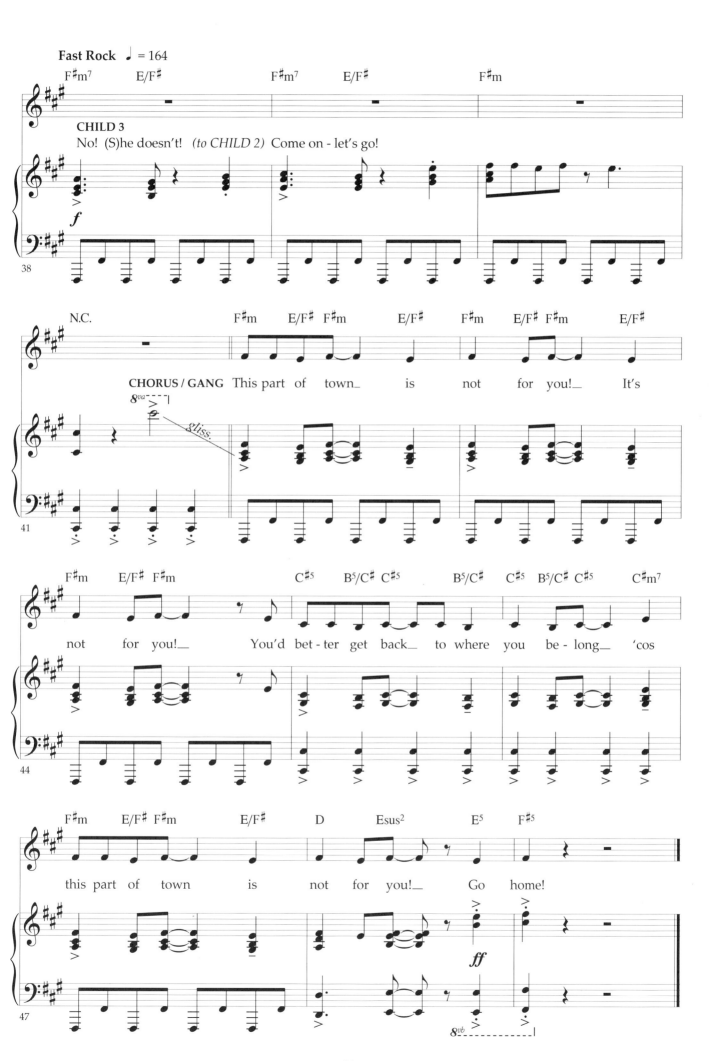

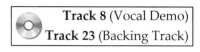
Out There

Music and Lyrics by Ruth Kenward

Arranged by Mark Dickman

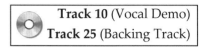

Someone Else's Eyes

Music and Lyrics by Ruth Kenward
Arranged by Mark Dickman

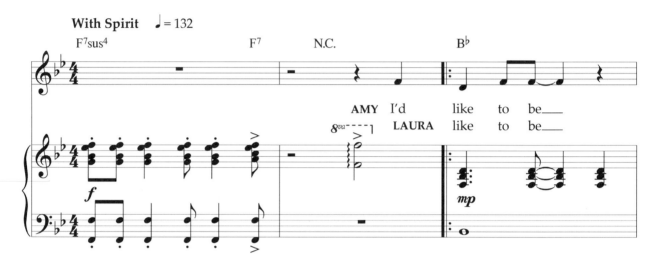

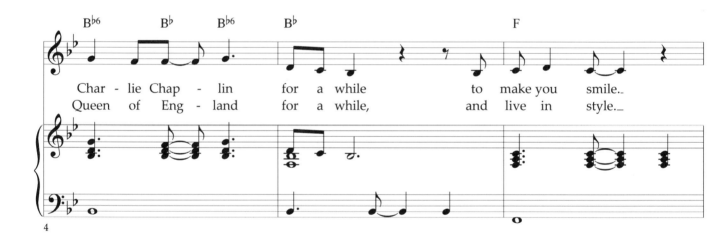

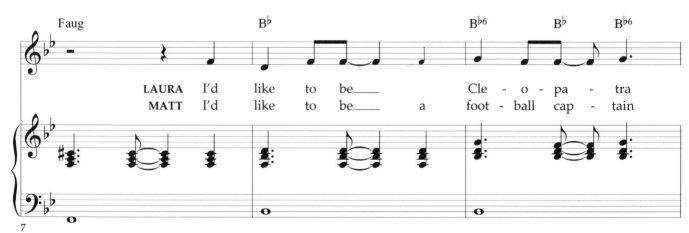

tend you're in their shoes!___ You can be an-y-one you choose,

Try their lives: go in dis-guise!___ See the world

through some-one else-'s eyes!

To Coda ⊕

1.

I'd

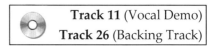
Out There (Reprise)

Music and Lyrics by Ruth Kenward
Arranged by Mark Dickman

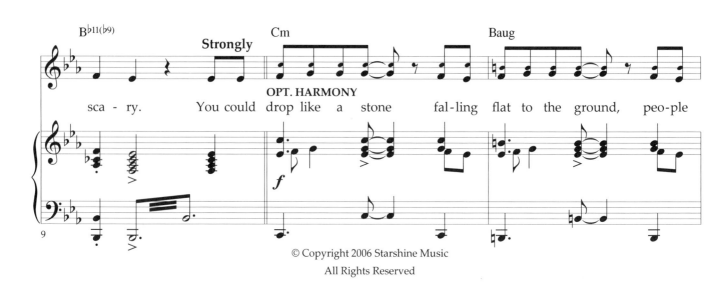

73

Bully!

Music and Lyrics by Ruth Kenward

Arranged by Mark Dickman

Track 13 (Vocal Demo)
Track 28 (Backing Track)

CHORUS
What turned you in-to a bul-ly? How did you get to be col-der than ice?___ What turned you in-to a bul-ly?

© Copyright 2006 Starshine Music
All Rights Reserved

74

77

Wrong Ain't Right

Music and Lyrics by Ruth Kenward
Arranged by Mark Dickman

Lively, with a strong beat ♩ = 100

N.C.

Fm   A♭

(rap, ad lib.)
ELLIE   What do I do that bothers you?   You pick on me no matter what I do.
JAKE   At the end of day, when you go to bed,   what kind of thoughts are in your head?

B♭   C   N.C.

You boss me about from mornin' to night.   Seems you're only happy when you pick a fight.
Are you pleased with the way you spent your day,   or maybe feelin' guilty 'bout the things you say?

Real Tough Stuff (Reprise)

Music and Lyrics by Ruth Kenward
Arranged by Mark Dickman

85

USEFUL ORGANISATIONS

The organisations listed below are helpful to children, parents and schools concerning bullying. All have web links to other relevant organisations, including some outside the UK.

ChildLine is the UK's free 24-hour helpline for children and young people, who can call **0800 1111** for help with any problem.

Textphone for children who are deaf, hard of hearing and speech impaired: **0800 400 222.**

Website - **www.childline.org.uk   Registered charity: 1003758**

Kidscape - the first charity in the UK established specifically to prevent bullying and child abuse.

Website - **www.kidscape.org.uk   Registered charity: 326864**

The helpline is for the use of parents, guardians or concerned relatives and friends of bullied children.
Phone: **020 7730 3300** Fax: **020 7730 7081** Helpline: **08451 205 204**

Working together to STOP **bullying**
The Anti-Bullying Alliance brings together over 65 organisations to create safe environments for children and young people and reduce bullying.

Website - **www.anti-bullyingalliance.org/index.htm**

Have you tried our other publications?

Our catalogue includes musicals, songs and cantatas for Christmas and all year round, with a range of material suitable for children from 5-13 years.

Full details of all our publications can be found at our website, where you can also listen to samples of **all** the songs.

www.starshine.co.uk

PERFORMING RIGHTS FOR THE SHOW

LICENCE APPLICATION

If you are planning to stage this musical, or to record the performance and/or songs, you will need to apply for a Licence. 'Block' licences which your school/group may have do not cover performances of musicals, licences for which are only available directly from publishers. To perform any musical <u>without</u> a specific licence to do so from its publisher is illegal.

Revenue raised from Performing Licences is the main source of income for writers. Licence charges vary according to publishers and performing circumstances, but our licence fees are very reasonable and safeguard you from prosecution. A quotation for your proposed production may be obtained from Starshine Music by phone /fax /e-mail.

To apply for a licence, complete the form below, and post or fax it to:
Starshine Music, Brown Cottage, Glynleigh Rd, Hankham, E. Sussex, England. BN24 5BJ.
Tel: +44 (0)1323 764334   Fax: +44 (0)1323 767145
Alternatively, e-mail us with the details: licences@starshine.co.uk

Please tell me the licence cost ☐   **Please process this application** ☐

APPLICATION TO PERFORM:

'Bully!' – by Ruth Kenward & Jo Sands

Name of school /group ....

Number of performances .... Date(s) of production...

Venue ....

Expected audience size per performance ....

Will admissions be charged (& if so, at what rate)? ....

Name of producer ....

Address of school /group ....

....

Postcode...

Daytime telephone number .... Fax: ....

e-mail address ....

If you are intending to record the show, or any part of it, please estimate the number of copies you will be producing. (Include an approximate figure to cover parents making video recordings, as well as any 'official' school recordings.)

VIDEO RECORDING	1-25	25-50	50-100	100+
SOUND RECORDING	1-25	25-50	50-100	100+

Song / Track Index

TITLE	CD DEMO	CD BACKING	SCORE PAGE
Where's Kim?	1	16	35
In The Gang	2	17	45
Real Tough Stuff	3	18	49
Sad Stuff (incidental)	4	19	---
Tough Stuff (incidental)	5	20	---
Make Time Go Backwards	6	21	53
Saturday	7	22	57
Out There	8	23	62
Go Backwards (incidental)	9	24	---
Someone Else's Eyes	10	25	66
Out There (short reprise)	11	26	72
Morning Music (incidental)	12	27	---
Bully!	13	28	74
Wrong Ain't Right	14	29	79
Real Tough Stuff (reprise)	15	30	83

View detailed information about all our products
and listen to samples of all our songs at:

www.starshine.co.uk